Share Some S

by Christina Gabbitas
illustrated by Ric Lumb

www.sharesomesecrets.com

My name is Billy and I live with my little sister Milly.
Our house is small but very cosy.
We have a neighbour called Noreen,
who is very nosey.

We have a cat called Bog.
Pancake is the name of our dog.

Pancake is very friendly
and wags his tail.
He brings a smile to
everyone's face without fail.

Bog is a different matter,
she walks away
as we start to chatter.

Mum shouts upstairs "Billy, Milly, Uncle Peter is here for lunch."

"Oh no! Do we have to listen to him munch?" says Milly.

4

We came downstairs and all sat down to eat.

Mum says "I have a secret that I want you to keep," as she sits up tall in her seat.
"I'm organising a surprise birthday party for Granny, and I'm getting some help from your Aunty Annie."

"That sounds nice," says Billy.
"Don't you think so Milly?" says Uncle Peter.
"Yes I think it sounds very nice," replies Milly.
"Please Mum, could we have some bakewell slice?"
"Of course we can, it's one of your Granny's favourite sweets. Granny always loves nice treats." replies Mum.

Billy and Milly leave the table
after finishing their cake.
They go to play in the garden, with their
dog Pancake.

"What's wrong Milly, you're not very chatty. I also don't think that you look very happy." says Billy.

"Do you think some of our secrets should be shared?" says Milly.
"I think so Milly, please don't be scared." says Billy.
"Uncle Peter said that I would
get into trouble and that I couldn't.
He said that no one would believe me, or like me,
so I shouldn't." says Milly.

"So you have a secret to share about Uncle Peter? Tell me Milly, I want to hear about it, you are my sister." says Billy.

"Uncle Peter said no one would like me if I tell." replies Milly.
"Has Uncle Peter got you under some kind of spell?" says Billy.

"Leave me alone, it makes me feel sad. Uncle Peter says that Mum will think I have done something bad." replies Milly.

"If you won't tell Mum or Stepdad, you could share your secret with your teacher, Mrs Herd?" says Billy. "Uncle Peter told me never to tell anyone and I feel really scared." replies Milly.

Milly and Billy set off for school the next day. "Why not tell Mrs Herd when everyone's gone out to play?" says Billy.
"I'm scared to tell, I really don't feel very well." replies Milly.

After their morning lesson, the bell rang for first break. Mrs Herd was sat at her desk, ready to have her coffee and cake.

Milly approaches Mrs Herd and asks "Please can I share my secret with you? Will you promise not to share it, or be angry with what I say or do?"

Mrs Herd replies, "That depends on the secret, as some secrets are better shared.
Whatever is the matter? You look very scared."

"My Uncle Peter said that bad things would happen to me. He says I would be in serious trouble. I...I...don't understand, you see? Uncle Peter always wants to look underneath my dress, it makes me feel uncomfortable and alone."

Mrs Herd replies, "Oh Milly, you have done something amazing today, just by telling me about how your Uncle Peter makes you feel in your home."

"Your clothes and underwear belong to you. No one can see what you don't want them to.

You can say no if it makes you uncomfortable, and it certainly won't get you into trouble." says Mrs Herd.

Mrs Herd calls Milly's parents, and invites them into school, to let them know what Milly has shared.

Milly's parents are upset, but grateful that Milly spoke to Mrs Herd.

"We are so pleased that you have shared a secret that made you feel sad. You are very brave Milly, and we are certainly not angry or mad." says Mum.

"Uncle Peter won't be visiting us again at our home. So you no longer need to feel sad or alone." says Stepdad.

"Thank you Mrs Herd for looking after Milly and being so understanding. I know your job can be very demanding." says Mum.

"We are very proud of Milly for sharing her secret with you Mrs Herd. It's important that her secret has been shared." says Stepdad.

"Well." says Mum. "It's Granny's party soon, we need to decorate the village hall room. Let's go shopping to see what we can find, the lady in the village shop is usually very kind."

They buy party poppers, streamers and a huge balloon. This is a very special balloon that plays the 'Happy Birthday' tune.

"Granny will love this, it will make her smile. A singing balloon is just her style." says Mum.

The big day arrived at the Village Hall.
A day for Granny to celebrate and have a ball.

Share Your Secret

Do you have a secret that you would like to share?
My teacher listened and she really did care.
Someone told me not to tell my secret.
They said no one would believe me
and that I should keep it.
My brother didn't like to see that I was sad.
I didn't feel comfortable telling Mum and Stepdad.
If you have a secret that is troubling you,
tell your teacher today.
They will be happy to help you, take some
of your troubles away.